HOUGHTON MIFFLIN

California
Science
Interactive
Text

HOUGHTON MIFFLIN   BOSTON

Printed in the U.S.A.

ISBN 13: 978-0-547-00461-7
ISBN 10: 0-547-00461-3

16   0928   16

4500587754

Contents

Plants

K W L

What Do You Know?

Talk with a partner.

List what you know about plants.

_____

_____

What plants do you see here?

_____

_____

Contents

 KWL

What Do You Want to Know?

Think about what you need to live. What might a plant need?

_____

_____

What do you wonder about plants?

_____

_____

VOCABULARY

sunlight Light from the Sun. *(noun)*

VOCABULARY ACTIVITY

Break It Apart

sunlight

Write the two smaller words in this big word.

_____ + _____

  2.b. Students know plants need water and light, and animals need water and food.

1 What Are the Needs of Plants?

Plants need air.

Plants need light.

Plants get light from the Sun.

Light from the Sun is called **sunlight**.

sunlight

Plants need water.

Some plants need a lot of water.

Some plants need a little water.

Circle the things a plant needs to grow. Write the words that name the things a plant needs.

space

trowel

light

pot

air

water

_____ _____

_____ _____

Summary

Plants need air, sunlight and water to grow. Draw a picture of a healthy plant.

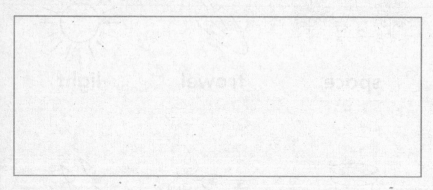

🎯 Compare and Contrast

How are the needs of plants alike?

Small plants	Big plants

6

Space to Grow

Plants need room to grow.

Room to grow is called space.

Big plants need a lot of space.

Small plants need a little space.

Compare and Contrast

How are the needs of plants alike?

What Are the Parts of Plants?

2

Plants have parts.
The parts help plants do
many things.

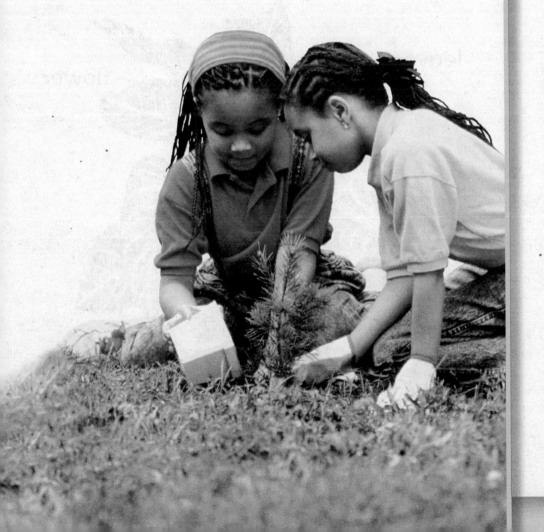

VOCABULARY

flower The part of a plant that makes seeds. *(noun)*

leaves Parts of a plant that make food for the plant. *(noun)*

roots Parts of a plant that take in water and hold the plant in the ground. *(noun)*

stem The part of a plant that connects the roots to the other plant parts and holds up the plant. *(noun)*

 2.a. Students know different plants and animals live in different environments and have parts that help them live there.
2.e. Students know roots take in water and nutrients. Green leaves make food from sunlight.

7

Write the name for each plant part.

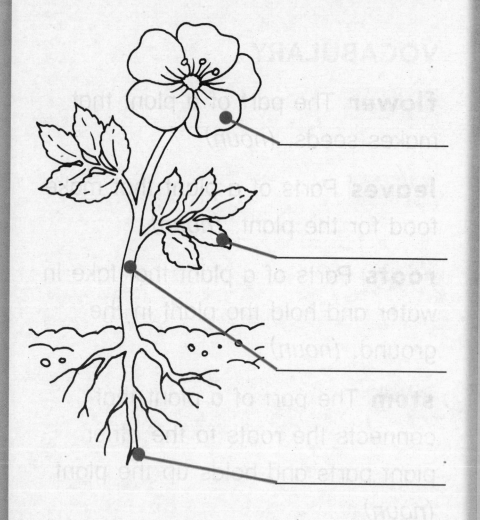

Plants have roots.
Plants have stems.
Plants have leaves.
Some plants have flowers.

leaves

flower

stem

roots

8

Parts of Plants

flower		A **flower** makes seeds.
leaves		**Leaves** make food for the plant.
stem		A **stem** holds up the plant.
roots		**Roots** get water from the ground.

Classify

Which part of the plant makes food?

Summary

Plants have parts. Each part helps the plant in some way.
Which plant part gets water from the ground?

_____

◎ **Classify** Which part of the plant makes food?

makes food	holds up plant	takes in water	makes seeds

VOCABULARY

soil The loose top layer of Earth. *(noun)*

nutrients Materials in the soil that plants need to grow. *(noun)*

VOCABULARY ACTIVITY

Use Words

nutrients

Circle words on page 8 that help you know what **nutrients** means.

  2.e. Students know roots take in water and nutrients. Green leaves make food from sunlight.

3 How Do Roots Help Plants?

Roots grow in soil.
Soil is the top layer of Earth.
Nutrients are things in the soil.
Plants need nutrients to grow.

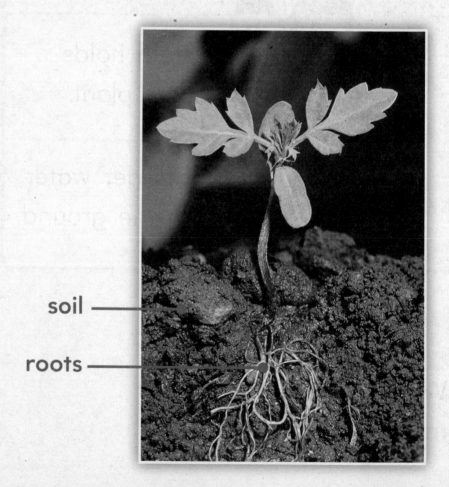

soil ——

roots ——

Roots take in water.

Roots take in nutrients.

Roots help hold up a plant.

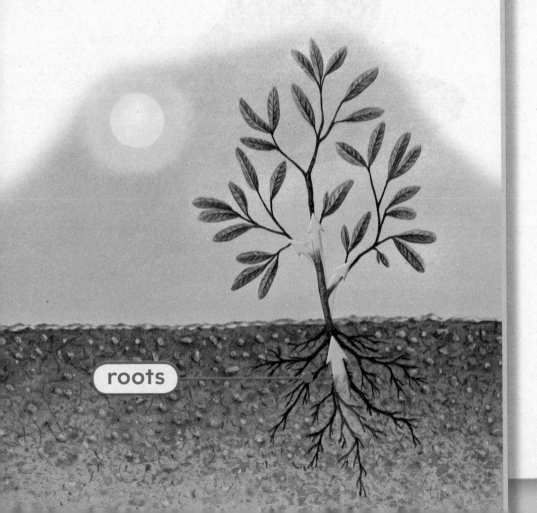

roots

Circle the part of each plant that takes in water and nutrients from soil. Write the name of the plant part.

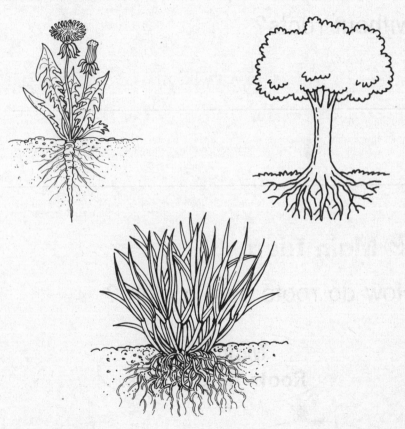

_____

Summary

Roots take in water and nutrients from soil.

What would happen to a plant without roots?

_____

_____

Main Idea

How do roots help a plant?

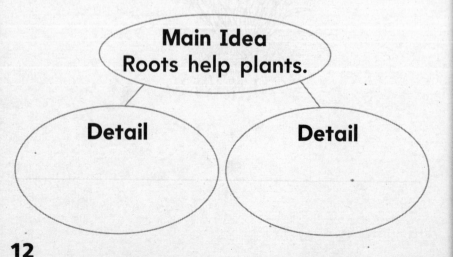

Main Idea
Roots help plants.

Detail

Detail

12

Different Kinds of Roots

People eat some roots.

Carrots and beets are roots.

People eat carrots and beets.

Main Idea

How do roots help a plant?

How Do Leaves Help Plants?

Plants need energy.
Energy is the power to change things.
Plants get energy from sunlight.

VOCABULARY

energy The power to cause change. (*noun*)

VOCABULARY ACTIVITY

Use Syllables

energy

Break the word into syllables.
Say each syllable aloud.
Clap once for each syllable.
How many syllables does the word **energy** have?

_____

 2.e. Students know roots take in water and nutrients. Green leaves make food from sunlight.
2.b. Students know plants need water and light, and animals need water and food.

13

I Wonder . . . I know plants need light. How would the plant on the left look if it got more light?

_____

_____

Change the picture to show how the plant would look.

All plants need light.
Plants need light to grow.
Plants will not grow well if they do not get the light they need.
The plant on the left did not get light.

How Leaves Work

Leaves take in sunlight.

Leaves take in air.

Leaves make food for the plant.

The plant uses the food to grow.

1. Plants get the energy they need

   from _____.

2. Draw the missing part of the plant that makes food for the plant. Then draw what gives plants energy.

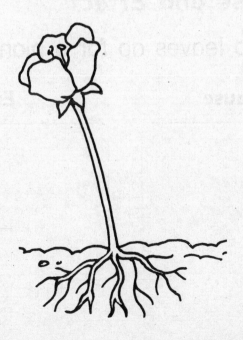

Summary

Plants get energy from sunlight.

Leaves make food for the plants.

How do leaves help plants grow?

_____

_____

◎ Cause and Effect

What do leaves do for a plant?

Cause	Effect
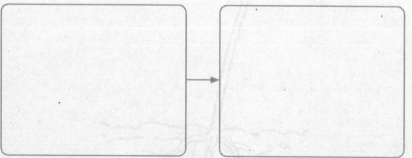

Different Kinds of Leaves

Leaves can be big.

Leaves can be small.

Leaves can be flat.

Leaves can have points.

leaves

Cause and Effect

What do leaves do for
a plant?

energy The power to cause change. Energy from the Sun warms land, air, and water.

energía Capacidad de causar cambios. La energía del Sol calienta la tierra, el aire y el agua.

flower The part of a plant that makes seeds.

flor La parte de una planta que produce semillas.

Draw lines to match the words with the same meaning.

nutrients   dirt

soil   food

17

Draw the parts of a plant that take in sunlight to make food.

18

leaves Parts of a plant that make food for the plant.

hojas Partes de una planta que producen su alimento.

nutrients Materials in the soil that plants need to grow. A plant takes in nutrients through its roots.

nutrientes Materiales del suelo que necesitan las plantas para crecer. Una planta toma nutrientes a través de sus raíces.

roots Parts of a plant that take in water and hold the plant in the ground.

raíces Partes de la planta que toman agua y mantienen a la planta sujeta al suelo.

Glossary

soil The loose top layer of Earth.

tierra La primera capa del suelo de la Tierra.

stem The part of a plant that connects the roots to the other plant parts and holds up the plant.

tallo Parte de la planta que conecta las raices con las otras partes de la planta y hace que la planta esté firme.

sunlight Light from the Sun.

luz solar Luz que proviene del Sol.

 Visit **www.eduplace.com** to play puzzles and word games.

Find the English words that are like these Spanish words. List the words in the chart.

Spanish Word	English Word
energía	
nutrientes	

KWL

What Did You Learn?

❶ Circle the correct answer.

❷ A plant needs _____

_____.

❸ Leaves help plants _____

_____.

❹ People can _____

_____.

Responding

Think About What You Have Read

❶ The power to cause change is

_____.

A) energy

B) nutrients

C) soil

❷ What does a plant need to live?

❸ How do leaves help plants?

❹ How can people help plants get what they need?

What Do You Know?

Draw an animal you know.
Name each of its body parts.

Animals

Contents

What Do You Want to Know?

What do you wonder about animals?

_____

_____

_____

_____

VOCABULARY

shelter A safe place for animals to live. *(noun)*

VOCABULARY ACTIVITY

Use Pictures

shelter

Look at the **shelter** on page 25. A picture helps you to know the meaning of the word. What do you know about this **shelter** from the picture?

24

2.b. Students know plants need water and light, and animals need water and food.
2.c. Students know animals eat plants or animals for food. Animals also use plants or animals for shelter.

1 What Are the Needs of Animals?

Animals need food.
Some animals eat plants.
Some animals eat other animals.

Shelter

Some animals need a shelter.
A **shelter** is a safe place for
animals to live.
A nest is a shelter.

nest

1. Draw a shelter that a bird uses.

2. Write a sentence about your
   picture. Use the word **shelter**.

_____

_____

3. Many animals use their

_____ to _____ in air.

4. Fish have _____ to take in air from water.

Animals Need Air and Water

Animals need air.
Some animals use a nose to get air.
Fish use gills to get air.

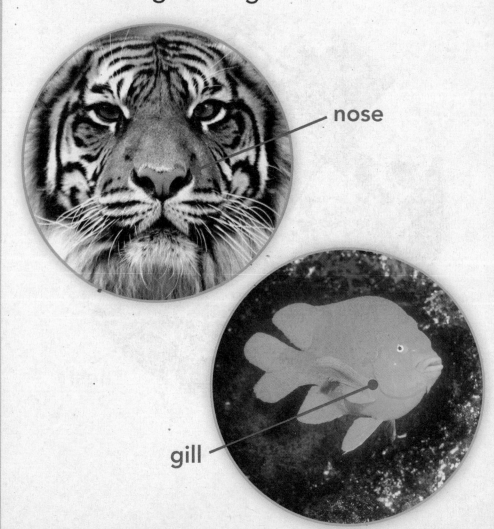

nose

gill

All animals need water.
Some animals get water by
drinking.

Draw Conclusions

How are all animals alike?

Summary

(Circle) the things animals need
to live.

pillow   water   food   air

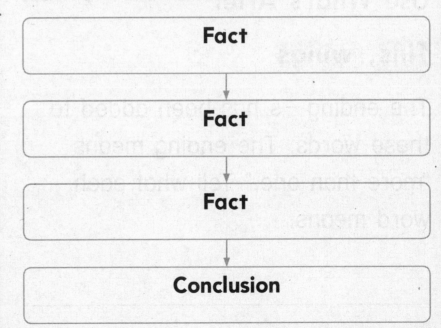 Draw Conclusions

How are animals alike?

Fact

↓

Fact

↓

Fact

↓

Conclusion

VOCABULARY

fins The body parts a fish uses to move in water. *(noun)*

wings The body parts a bird uses to fly through the air. *(noun)*

VOCABULARY ACTIVITY

Use What's After

fins, **wings**

The ending –s has been added to these words. The ending means "more than one." Tell what each word means.

  2.a. Students know different plants and animals live in different environments and have parts that help them live there.

2 What Are the Parts of Animals?

Animals have body parts.
The parts help animals find food.
The parts help animals stay safe.

bush baby

ears

eyes

legs

quills

stinger

claws

smell

sound

color and shape

1. Circle the body parts of each animal that helps it to stay safe.

2. Write the name of the animal under each picture.

29

3. A  uses _____ and

_____ to move in water.

4. A uses _____ to fly
through the air.

Parts for Moving

Body parts help animals move.

A fish uses a tail to move.

A fish uses **fins** to move, too.

fin

tail

Some animals walk.
They use legs to walk.
Some animals fly.
They use **wings** to fly.

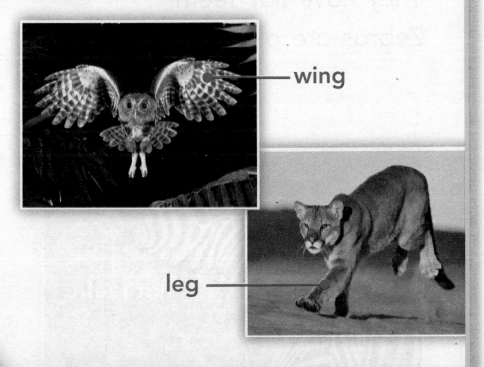

wing

leg

Main Idea

Why do many animals have legs?

Summary

Name the body parts animals use to help them live.

_____

_____

_____

🎯 **Main Idea** Why do many animals have legs?

Main Idea
Animals have legs.

Detail

Detail

VOCABULARY

plant eater An animal that eats mostly plants. *(noun)*

meat eater An animal that eats other animals. *(noun)*

VOCABULARY ACTIVITY

Classify Words

plant eater, **meat eater**

Sort animals by what they eat.
List animals that eat plants.
List animals that eat animals.

3 How Do Animals Use Their Mouths?

Some animals eat plants.
They are **plant eaters**.
They have flat teeth.
Zebras are plant eaters.

flat teeth

2.d. Students know what animals eat from the shape of their teeth.

Some animals eat other animals.

They are **meat eaters**.

They have sharp teeth.

Lions are meat eaters.

sharp teeth

1. Draw food that a zebra eats.

2. Draw food that a lion eats.

3. Draw a bear's teeth.

I **Wonder . . .** Dogs have sharp teeth. What kind of food can dogs eat?

_____

Some animals eat plants and animals.
They have flat teeth.
They have sharp teeth, too.
Bears eat plants and animals.
They have flat teeth and sharp teeth.

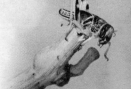

Other Mouth Parts

Some animals do not have teeth.
They have other parts.
The parts help them eat.
This animal uses its long tongue
to get food.

zebra   lion   chameleon

4. This animal uses its flat teeth to

   grind plants. _____

5. This animal uses its sharp teeth

   to tear meat. _____

6. This animal uses its long tongue

   to catch food. _____

Summary

Animals use their mouths to eat.
Which teeth do plant eaters have?

_____

Which teeth do meat eaters have?

_____

◎ Compare and Contrast

How are a lion's teeth different
from a zebra's teeth?

Lion's Teeth	Zebra's Teeth

Birds have beaks.
A beak helps a bird eat.

beak

Compare and Contrast

How are a lion's teeth different
from a zebra's teeth?

fins The body parts a fish uses to move in water.

aletas Las partes del cuerpo con las que un pez se mueve en el agua.

fin

meat eater An animal that eats other animals. A meat eater has sharp teeth.

carnívoro Animal que se come a otros animales. Un carnívoro tiene dientes afilados.

plant eater An animal that eats mostly plants. A plant eater has flat teeth.

herbívoro Animal que come mayormente plantas. Un herbívoro tiene dientes planos.

Pick two science words. Write each word three times.

_____ _____ _____

_____ _____ _____

Work with a partner.
Test each other on the spelling.

Visit **www.eduplace.com** to play puzzles and word games.

(Circle) the English words and their meanings for all the science words.

Glossary

shelter A safe place for animals to live.

refugio Lugar seguro donde viven los animales.

shelter

wings The body parts a bird uses to fly through the air.

alas Parte del cuerpo que un ave utiliza para volar por el aire.

wing

Responding

Think About What You Have Read

❶ A safe place for animals to live is _____.

  A) fins

  B) wings

  C) shelter

❷ Why does a fish have fins?

❸ What do animals need to live?

❹ Why isn't a bicycle an animal?

What Did You Learn?

❶ Circle the correct answer.

❷ A fish has fins to _____

_____.

❸ Animals need _____

_____.

❹ A bicycle is not an animal because

_____.

What Do You Know?

Talk with a partner.

List living things.

Tell what they need to.live.

_____

_____

_____

Living Things Meet Their Needs

Contents

What Do You Want to Know?

What do you wonder about how living things get what they need?

_____

_____

_____

_____

_____

_____

41

VOCABULARY

living thing Something that needs air, food, water, and space to live. *(noun)*

nonliving thing Something that does not need food, water, and air to live. *(noun)*

environment All of the living and nonliving things around a living thing. *(noun)*

1 What Is an Environment?

A **living thing** needs air and space.
It needs food and water.
Plants are living things.
Animals are living things.

2.a. Students know different plants and animals live in different environments and have parts that help them live there.
2.b. Students know plants need water and light, and animals need water and food.

A **nonliving thing** does not
need air.
It does not need food or water.
Water is a nonliving thing.
Soil is a nonliving thing.
Rocks are nonliving things.

1. Circle the living things in this
environment.

2. Put an X over the nonliving
things in this environment.

I Wonder . . . I know that the ocean is an environment.
What living things are in an ocean?

_____

_____

_____

44

Plants and animals live in an environment.
An **environment** has living things and nonliving things.
The ocean is an environment.

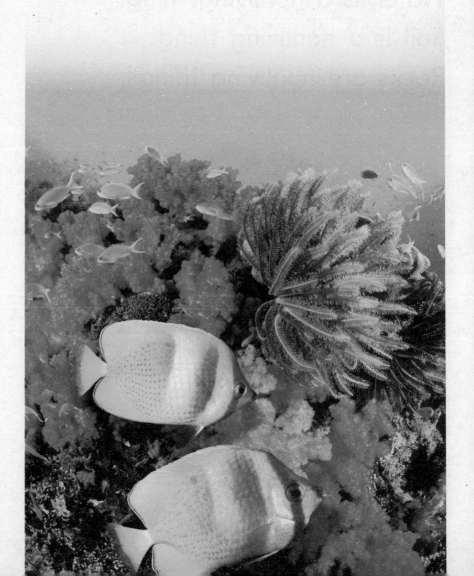

Different Environments

Some environments are hot.

Some are cold.

Some are wet.

Some are dry.

desert

Main Idea

What can you find in an environment?

Summary

An environment is a place where living and nonliving things are found. Tell how an ocean and desert are different.

_____

_____

🎯 **Main Idea**   What can you find in an environment?

Main Idea
An environment has living and nonliving things

Detail

Detail

45

VOCABULARY

energy The power to cause change. *(noun)*

food chain The order in which energy moves from one thing to another. *(noun)*

VOCABULARY ACTIVITY

Use Pictures

food chain

Use the picture on page 48. Draw arrows to show how energy moves in a food chain.

 2.c. Students know animals eat plants or animals for food. Animals also use plants or animals for shelter.
2.b. Students know plants need water and light, and animals need water and food.

2 How Do Living Things Get Energy?

Energy is the power to change things.
Living things get energy from food.
It helps them grow and change.
A bird eats to get energy.

Food Chains

A **food chain** shows how energy gets from one thing to another. Most food chains start with the Sun. Plants use sunlight to make food.

They get energy.

Draw an arrow to show where plants get energy from.

Summary

Living things get energy from food.

Food chains start with the Sun.

How do you get energy?

Sequence

How do animals get energy?

↓

An animal eats the plant to get energy.

↓

48

Animals eat the plants.

They get energy.

Some animals eat other animals.

They get energy.

This is a food chain.

Sequence

How do animals get energy?

Where Do Animals Find Shelter?

Animals need shelter.

Shelter is a safe place.

Animals live in a shelter.

A deer finds shelter under a tree.

VOCABULARY

shelter A safe place for animals to live. *(noun)*

VOCABULARY ACTIVITY

Use Words

shelter

Animals live in a **shelter**.
Use clues from the sentence above to help you know what **shelter** means.

_____

_____

 2.c. Students know animals eat plants or animals for food. Animals also use plants or animals for shelter.

Label the pictures to show where animals find shelter.

_____   _____

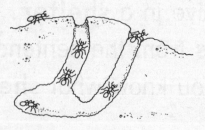

_____

Animals find shelter in plants or in the ground.
They find shelter in water and on other animals, too.
A flea finds shelter on a dog.

flea

Animals Build Shelters

Animals can make new shelters.
Some insects make nests.
Birds make nests, too.

nest

Classify

What animals live on other animals?

Summary

Animals need shelter to stay safe.
List places where animals find shelter.

a. _____

b. _____

Classify

What animals live on other animals?

Animals That Live on Other animals	Animals They Live On

VOCABULARY

structures Parts that help plants and animals live in their environments. *(noun)*

VOCABULARY ACTIVITY

Use Syllables

structures

Break the word into syllables.
Say each syllable aloud.
Clap once for each syllable.
How many syllables are in **structures**?

 2.a. Students know different plants and animals live in different environments and have parts that help them live there.

4 How Do Plants and Animals Live in Different Places?

Plants live in different environments.
Animals live in different environments.
They have parts that help them live.
These parts are called **structures**.

giraffe

A bird has a beak.

A giraffe has a long neck.

A water lily has long stems.

These structures help them get food.

water lily

1. Circle the structure on the giraffe that helps it get food.

2. Circle the structure on the water lily that helps it get energy.

53

Summary

Different plants and animals live in different environments. Pick an animal or plant. What structures does it have to help it live in its environment?

🎯 Draw Conclusions

How do structures help an animal?

Fact

↓

Fact

↓

Conclusion
Animals have structures that help them live in their environment.

Structures That Protect

A rose has thorns.
A camel has big feet.
Some fish look like rocks.
These structures keep them safe.

Draw Conclusions

How do structures help an animal?

energy The power to cause change. Energy from the Sun warms land, air, and water.

energía Capacidad de causar cambios. La energía del Sol calienta la tierra, el aire y el agua.

environment All of the living and nonliving things around a living thing.

medio ambiente Todos los seres vivos y las cosas sin vida que rodean a un ser vivo.

Read each science word on this page. Write the word that ends in the letter **t**.

_____

(Circle) the science words that have a **ch** or **th** digraph.

food chain The order in which energy moves from one thing to another.

cadena alimenticia El orden en que la energía se mueve de una cosa a otra.

living thing Something that needs air, food, water, and space to live. Plants and animals are living things.

ser vivo Algo que necesita aire, alimento, agua y un espacio para vivir. Las plantas y los animales son seres vivos.

Glossary

nonliving thing Something that does not need food, water, and air to live. Rocks are nonliving things.

cosa sin vida Algo que no necesita alimento, agua o aire para vivir. Las rocas son cosas sin vida.

shelter A safe place for animals to live.

refugio Lugar seguro donde viven los animales.

structures Parts that help plants and animals live in their environments.

estructuras Partes que ayudan a las plantas y animales en el medio ambiente.

 Visit **www.eduplace.com** to play puzzles and word games.

Find the English word that is like this Spanish word. Write the word in the chart.

Spanish Word	English Word
energía	

KWL

What Did You Learn?

❶ Circle the correct answer.

❷ Plants use sunlight to _____.

❸ Environments are different

because _____.

❹ Animals need both living things
and nonliving things for

_____.

Responding

Think About What You Have Read

❶ A safe place for animals to
live is _____.

   A) a food chain
   B) a shelter
   C) an environment

❷ How do plants use sunlight?

❸ In what ways are environments
different?

❹ Why do animals need both
living things and nonliving
things?

KWL

What Do You Know?

Talk with a partner.

List places where animals live. Tell what you find there.

_____

_____

_____

_____

Kinds of Environments

Contents

What Do You Want to Know?

What do you wonder about the places where animals live?

_____

_____

_____

_____

_____

_____

VOCABULARY

habitat A part of an environment where a plant or an animal lives. *(noun)*

coast A land and water habitat along an ocean. *(noun)*

VOCABULARY ACTIVITY

Use Pictures

coast

Say the word aloud. Use the pictures to help you know what **coast** means.

  2.a. Students know different plants and animals live in different environments and have parts that help them live there.

1 What Lives Along a Coast?

A **habitat** is where a plant or animal lives.

A **coast** is a habitat.

It is the water in the ocean.

It is the land by the ocean, too.

A coast has plants and animals.
These are living things.
A coast has water and rocks.
These are nonliving things.

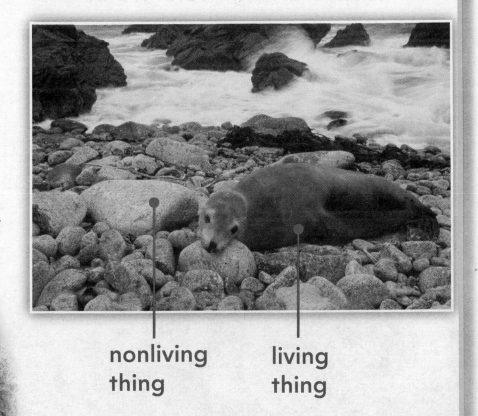

nonliving
thing

living
thing

I. Write the correct science words next to each meaning.

a. A land and water habitat

along an ocean. _____

b. A part of an environment

where a plant or animal

lives. _____

2. What body parts does an otter have that help it live along a coast?

_____

_____

_____

I Wonder . . . Many living things live along a coast. What other animals live there?

_____

_____

Life Along a Coast

Living things have parts.

Parts help some plants and animals:

- live in a coast habitat
- find food
- keep warm in cold water

otter

This bird is a pelican.
A pelican lives on a coast.
It has a big mouth.
The mouth holds fish.
The pelican has feet that
help it swim.

big mouth

webbed feet

Main Idea

What parts help a pelican live along the coast?

Summary

Some animals have body parts that help them live along a coast. What parts help a sea lion live there?

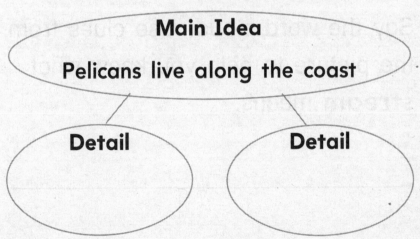

Main Idea What parts help a pelican live along the coast?

Main Idea

Pelicans live along the coast

Detail

Detail

VOCABULARY

stream A small river. *(noun)*

VOCABULARY ACTIVITY

Use Pictures

stream

Say the word aloud. Use clues from the picture to help you know what **stream** means.

_____

  2.a. Students know different plants and animals live in different environments and have parts that help them live there.

2 What Lives in a Stream?

A **stream** is a small river.
A stream has plants and animals.
These are living things.
A stream has fresh water and rocks.
These are nonliving things.

nonliving thing

stream

living thing

Living things get water from the stream.

They eat plants and animals in or by the stream.

Raccoons find food in a stream.

1. Draw the living and nonliving things in a stream.

2. A fish uses its _____ and

_____ to swim in a stream.

3. Why does a turtle have a
hard shell?

_____

_____

_____

Life in a Stream

Living things have parts.
Parts help some plants and
animals live in a stream habitat.

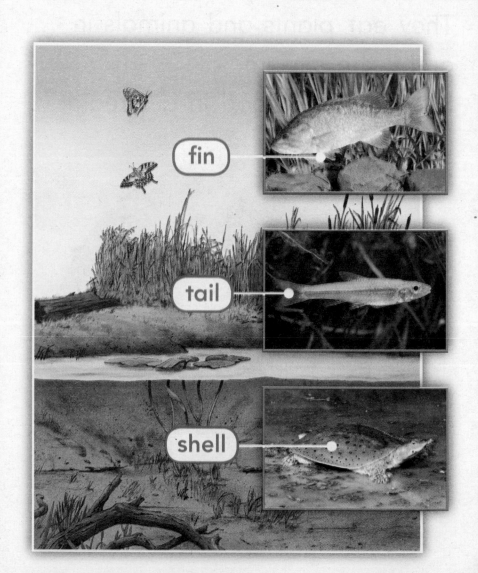

fin

tail

shell

This bird is a heron.
A heron has long legs.
The legs help it walk in water.

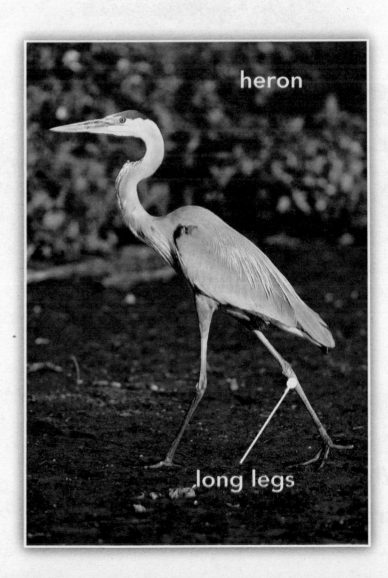

heron

long legs

4. What body parts help a heron live in a stream?

_____

_____

Summary

Living things have parts that help them live in a stream. What part helps a turtle live there?

⊙ **Draw Conclusions** What nonliving things in a stream do animals use?

Fact

↓

Fact

↓

Conclusion Animals use nonliving things in a stream.

Some plants have long stems. The stems let the leaves reach sunlight.

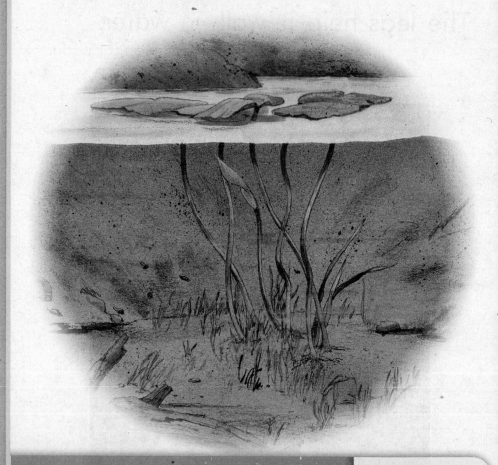

Draw Conclusions

What nonliving things in a stream do animals use?

What Lives on a Mountain?

3

A **mountain** is a high piece of land.

Many things live low on a mountain.

It can be warm.

There are many trees and plants.

mountain

VOCABULARY

mountain A high part of Earth's surface. *(noun)*

VOCABULARY ACTIVITY

Use Pictures

mountain

A picture helps you know the meaning of words. What do you know about a **mountain** from this picture?

_____

 2.a. Students know different plants and animals live in different environments and have parts that help them live there.

71

1. What is a mountaintop like?

_____

_____

2. Draw a mountaintop. Draw an animal that lives there.

Living on Mountaintops

The top of a mountain is the mountaintop.

Few things live on the mountaintop.

It can be cold on a mountaintop.

It can also be windy.

Living things have parts.
Parts help some plants and
animals live on a mountaintop.
A bighorn sheep has feet like
rubber to help it walk on rocks.

3. How is the top of a mountain
different from the low part of
the mountain?

Low Part of Mountain	Mountaintop

Summary

Different plants and animals live on different parts of a mountain. Name the parts of a mountain.

Compare and Contrast

Why do more animals and plants live low on a mountain?

Many Animals Low on Mountain	Few Animals on Mountaintop

Animals on a mountaintop have thick fur.
It keeps them warm.

fur

Compare and Contrast

Why do more animals and plants live low on a mountain?

coast A land and water habitat along an ocean.

costa Hábitat formado por tierra y agua a lo largo de un océano.

habitat A part of an environment where a plant or an animal lives.

hábitat Parte del medio ambiente donde vive una planta o un animal.

Choose one science word. Cut out a picture of the word. Glue the picture here. Write the word.

_____

Visit **www.eduplace.com** to play puzzles and word games.

Find the English words that are like these Spanish words. List the words in the chart.

Spanish Word	English Word
costa	
hábitat	
montaña	

Glossary

mountain A high part of Earth's surface.

montaña Parte alta de la superficie de la Tierra.

stream A small river.

arroyo Río pequeño.

Think About What You Have Read

❶ A small river is a

_____.

A) stream

B) habitat

C) coast

❷ Where do sea lions and pelicans live?

❸ Why are there few living things on mountaintops?

❹ How can you predict where an animal might live?

KWL

What Did You Learn?

❶ Circle the correct answer.

❷ Sea lions and pelicans live

_____.

❸ There are few living things on

mountaintops because _____

_____.

❹ You can predict where an animal

might live by _____

_____.

Weather

KWL

What Do You Know?

Talk with a partner.

Tell about today's weather.

Tell about yesterday's weather.

_____

_____

_____

Weather

Contents

What Do You Want to Know?

What else do you wonder about weather?

_____

_____

_____

_____

_____

_____

_____

VOCABULARY

weather What the air outside is like. (*noun*)

VOCABULARY ACTIVITY

Classify Words

weather

Weather is what the air outside is like. What kinds of **weather** do you know?

_____

_____

3.b. Students know that the weather changes from day to day but you can predict weather during a season.

1 How Does Weather Change?

Weather is what the air outside is like.

There are many kinds of weather.

Weather may be warm.

It may be cool.

sunny

Weather may be rainy.
It may be sunny.
It may be cloudy.
It may be windy.

rainy

1. A sunny day is _____ and

   _____. On sunny days I like

   to _____.

2. A rainy day is _____ and

   _____. On rainy days I like

   to _____

   _____.

3. Name each kind of weather.

a.  _____

b. 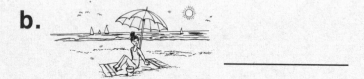 _____

c. 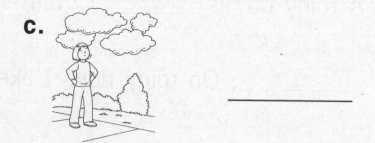 _____

d. 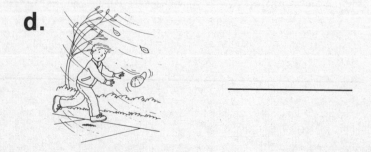 _____

We can see clouds.

We can feel warm air.

We can hear rain.

We can see wind move things.

windy and cloudy

Ways Weather Changes

Monday	cloudy	
Tuesday	rainy	
Wednesday	sunny	

I Wonder . . . Weather changes from day to day. At noon it is warm and sunny. Later it begins to rain. How did the sky change?

_____

_____

_____

Summary

Weather changes from day to day.
Tell about weather you know.

_____

_____

Main Idea How might weather change from day to day?

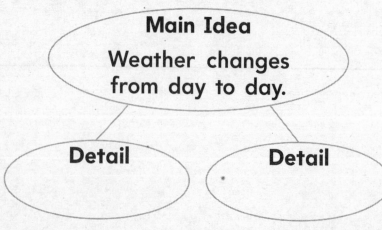

Main Idea

Weather changes from day to day.

Detail   Detail

84

Weather Changes

Weather changes every day.
Today it may be sunny.
Tomorrow it may be cloudy.

clouds

Main Idea

How might weather change from day to day?

How Are Weather Tools Used?

2

We use tools to learn about weather.

A **thermometer** is a tool that measures temperature. **Temperature** is how warm or cool something is.

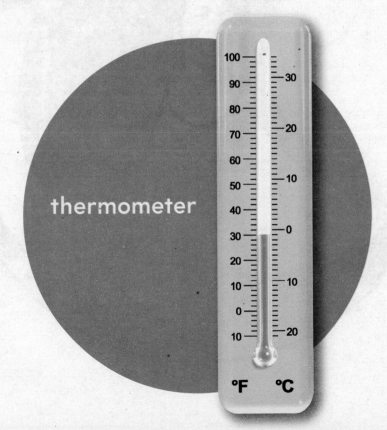

thermometer

VOCABULARY

thermometer A tool that measures temperature. *(noun)*

temperature How warm or cool something is. *(noun)*

wind vane A tool that shows which way the wind blows. *(noun)*

VOCABULARY ACTIVITY

Use Words

thermometer

Circle words on the page that tell what a **thermometer** is.

3.a. Students know how to use simple tools to measure weather.

1. Tell about the weather in this picture.

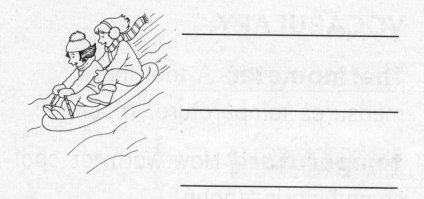

_____

_____

_____

2. Tell about the weather in this picture.

_____

_____

When it is cold, we wear warm clothes.

When it is warm, we wear clothes to keep us cool.

86

Tools for Wind and Rain

Tools help us learn about wind.
A **wind vane** is a tool.
It shows which way wind blows.

3. What tool measures temperature?

_____

Draw it.

_____

4. What tool shows which way the wind blows?

_____

Draw it.

Summary

You can use tools to measure weather.

Name tools that measure weather.

_____

_____

Draw Conclusions

If you need a coat, what can you tell about the temperature?

FACT

↓

Conclusion

88

Tools help us learn about rain.
A rain gauge is a tool.
It tells us how much it has rained.

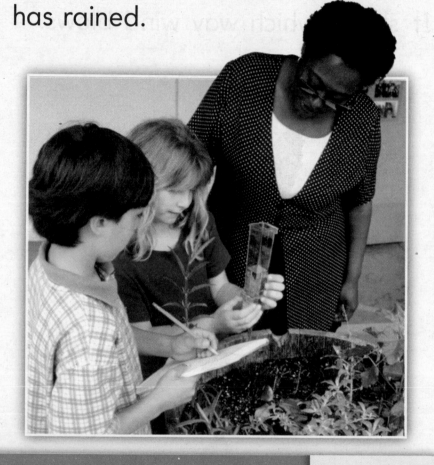

Draw Conclusions

If you need a coat, what can you tell about the temperature?

What Warms Land, Air, and Water?

Energy is the power to change things.

Energy comes from the Sun.

It warms everything on Earth.

VOCABULARY

energy The power to cause change. *(noun)*

shadows What forms when an object blocks light. *(noun)*

VOCABULARY ACTIVITY

Use Syllables

energy

Break the word into syllables.

Clap once for each syllable.

How many syllables are in **energy**?

_____

3.c. Students know the sun warms the land, air, and water.

89

I. Tell what the Sun warms in each picture.

a.

The Sun warms the

_____.

b.

The Sun warms the

_____.

The Sun warms Earth's land.
It warms sand and sidewalks.
The Sun warms Earth's water.
It warms lakes and ponds.

The Sun warms Earth's air, too.
The Sun warms things in the day.
It does not warm things at night.

I Wonder . . . Air, land, and water feel warmer in the day. Why?

_____

_____

_____

_____

3. Circle the shadow.
Where would the Sun have to be
to make this shadow?
Add the Sun to the picture.

_____

Shadows

A **shadow** is made
when something blocks light.
A place with a shadow
is called shade.
This tree makes a shadow.

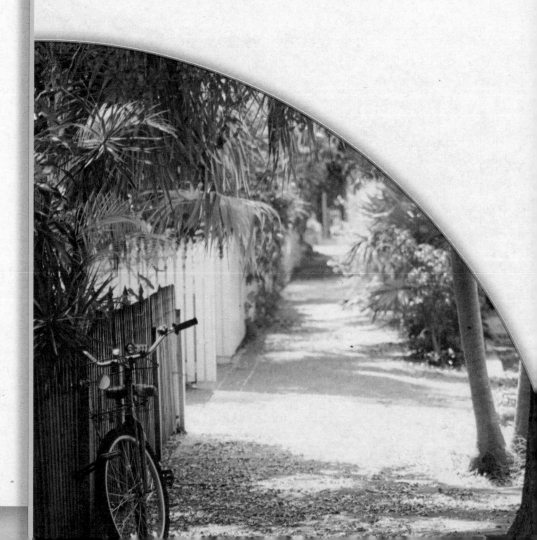

Clouds can block sunlight.
Clouds can make shadows.
The air may feel cool on
cloudy days.

Cause and Effect

What causes a shadow?

Summary

Energy from the Sun warms Earth.
Name the parts of Earth that the
Sun warms.

_____

_____

Cause and Effect

What causes a shadow?

Cause	Effect
	A shadow forms.

93

Choose three science words. Make up a story that uses your words. Tell a partner your story.

energy The power to cause change. Energy from the Sun warms land, air, and water.

energía Capacidad de causar cambios. La energía del Sol calienta la tierra, el aire y el agua.

shadow What forms when an object blocks light.

sombra Lo que se forma cuando un objeto bloquea la luz.

Glossary

temperature How warm or cool something is.

temperatura Lo cálido o frío que está una cosa.

thermometer A tool that measures temperature.

termómetro Instrumento que mide la temperatura.

weather What the air outside is like.

tiempo Cómo está el aire fuera de la casa.

wind vane A tool that shows which way the wind blows.

veleta Instrumento que muestra la dirección del viento.

Visit **www.eduplace.com** to play puzzles and word games.

Find the English words that are like these Spanish words. List the words in the chart.

Spanish Word	English Word
energía	
temperatura	
termómetro	

95

Chapter Review

What Did You Learn?

❶ Circle the correct answer.

❷ It is cooler at night because ____

_____.

❸ Weather can be _____

_____.

❹ I know it is windy because _____

_____.

Responding

Think About What You Have Read

❶ A tool that measures temperature is _____.

   A) energy

   B) a thermometer

   C) a shadow

❷ Why is it cooler at night than during the day?

❸ What are some ways weather changes?

❹ How do you know that it is windy if you cannot see wind?

KWL

What Do You Know?

Talk with a partner.

List seasons you know.

Write about weather for one season.

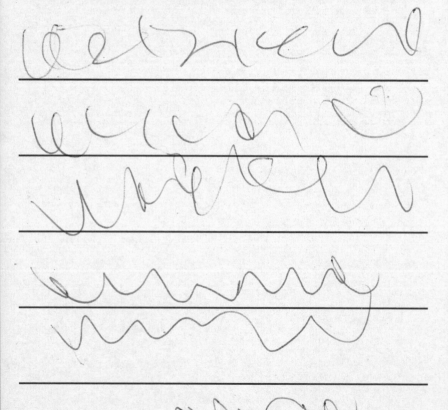

Seasons

Contents

What Do You Want to Know?

What do you wonder about the four seasons?

_____

_____

_____

_____

_____

VOCABULARY

season A time of year that has its own kind of weather. *(noun)*

winter The season that follows fall. *(noun)*

VOCABULARY ACTIVITY

Use Pictures

winter

Look at the picture of **winter**. What is **winter** like?

_____

_____

  3.b. Students know that the weather changes from day to day but you can predict weather during a season.
3.a. Students know how to use simple tools to measure weather.

1 What Is Winter Weather?

A **season** is a time of year. A season has its own kind of weather.

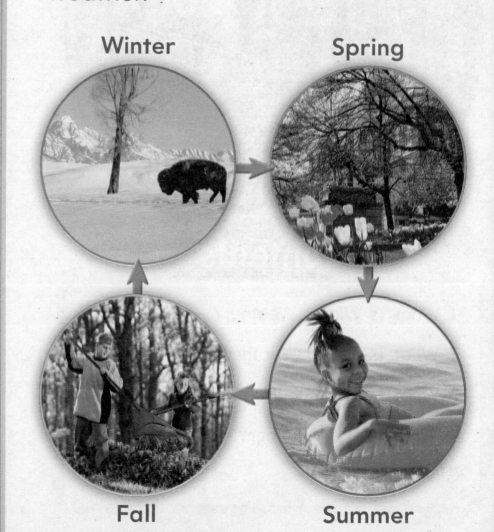

Winter

Spring

Fall

Summer

Winter is a season.

It comes after fall.

There is less sunlight in winter.

That means winter is cold.

It is colder than the
other seasons.

1. Circle the words that tell about winter.

2. Write a sentence about winter.

_____

_____

3. Draw a plant in winter.

Winter is hard for plants and animals.

It can be hard for animals to find food.

Some plants die.

Some plants rest.

Winter in Different Places

Winter is different in different places.

Winter is very cold in some places.

Winter is only a little cooler than summer in other places.

Winter can be wet.

It can be dry.

Cause and Effect

What happens to plants when the weather gets cooler?

Summary

Winter is the coldest season. Tell about winter weather where you live.

_____

_____

Cause and Effect

What happens to plants when the weather gets cooler?

Cause	Effect
The weather gets cooler. →	

VOCABULARY

spring The season that follows winter. *(noun)*

VOCABULARY ACTIVITY

Find All the Meanings

spring

A word can have more than one meaning. You may know that to **spring** is to bounce. The word **spring** also is the name of a season.

3.b. Students know that the weather changes from day to day but you can predict weather during a season.
3.a. Students know how to use simple tools to measure weather.

2 What Is Spring Weather?

Spring is a season.
It comes after winter.
Spring is warmer than winter.
There is more rain in spring, too.

Plants grow in spring.
Flowers bloom in spring.
Many animals are born in spring, too.

1. Circle the words that tell about spring.

Write **winter** or **spring** to make each sentence true.

2. Weather gets warmer.

_____

3. The coldest season of the year.

_____

4. Many new plants grow.

_____

Summary

Weather gets warmer in spring.
Why do more plants grow in spring
than in winter?

_____

_____

🎯 Main Idea

How can you tell it is spring?

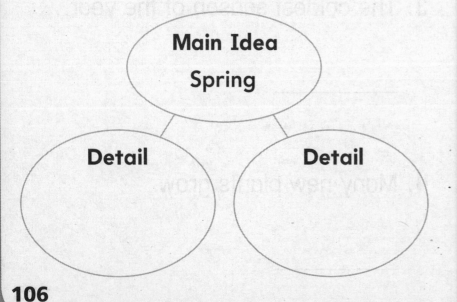

Main Idea

Spring

Detail   Detail

Spring in Different Places

Spring is different in different
places.
Spring can be warm.
It can be cool.

Main Idea

How can you tell it is spring?

What Is Summer Weather?

Summer is a season.

It comes after spring.

Summer is the warmest season.

It gets the most sunlight.

VOCABULARY

summer The season that follows spring. *(noun)*

VOCABULARY ACTIVITY

Use Syllables

summer

Break the word into syllables. Say each syllable aloud. Clap once for each syllable. How many syllables does **summer** have?

——————

 3.b. Students know that the weather changes from day to day but you can predict weather during a season.
3.c. Students know the sun warms the land, air, and water.

107

1. Name words that tell about summer.

_____

_____

2. Draw a picture of summer. Show what you like to do in summer.

Plants grow in the summer.
Young animals grow, too.
They learn to find food.

Summer in Different Places

Summer is different in different places.

Summer can be very hot.

It can be wet.

It can be dry.

Compare and Contrast

How are spring and summer different?

Summary

Summer is the warmest season of the year.

Tell about summer where you live.

_____

_____

Compare and Contrast

How are spring and summer different?

Spring	Summer

109

VOCABULARY

fall The season that follows summer. *(noun)*

VOCABULARY ACTIVITY

Find All the Meanings

fall

A word can have more than one meaning.

You may know that to **fall** is to drop.

The word **fall** also is the name of a season.

  3.b. Students know that the weather changes from day to day but you can predict weather during a season.

4 What Is Fall Weather?

Fall is a season.

It comes after summer.

There is less sunlight in fall.

It is not as warm as summer.

Some leaves change color.
They fall to the ground.
Farm crops die.
Animals get ready for winter.

I Wonder . . . Trees change
with each season. Choose one tree.
Draw how it looks in two seasons.
Label each picture with the season.

Summary

The weather is cooler in fall.
List words that tell about fall.

_____

_____

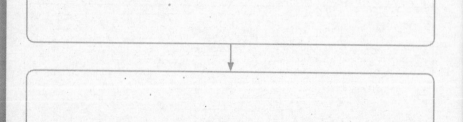 **Sequence**

What season comes after summer?

┌─────────────────────────────┐
│   │
│   │
└─────────────────────────────┘
            ↓
┌─────────────────────────────┐
│   │
│   │
└─────────────────────────────┘

Fall in Different Places

Fall is different in different places.
Fall is cooler than summer.
It can be wet.
It can be dry.

Sequence

What season comes after summer?

fall The season that follows summer.

otoño La estación que sigue al verano.

season A time of year that has its own kind of weather.

estación Época del año que tiene su propio tiempo.

spring The season that follows winter. Weather begins to get warmer in spring.

primavera Estación que sigue al invierno. El tiempo se vuelve más cálido en la primavera.

Write each science word on a card.

Bring the cards home.

Share them with your family.

Unscramble this word **lafl**

_____

Visit **www.eduplace.com** to play puzzles and word games.

(Circle) the English words and their meanings for all the science words.

Glossary

summer The season that follows spring. Summer is the warmest season.

verano La estación que sigue a la primavera. El verano es la estación más cálida.

winter The season that follows fall.

invierno La estación que sigue al otoño.

Think About What You Have Read

❶ The warmest season is

_____.

A) fall

B) spring

C) summer

❷ What is a season?

❸ How does weather change from summer to fall?

❹ Tell how thermometers can help you understand spring weather.

KWL

What Did You Learn?

❶ (Circle) the correct answer.

❷ A season is _____

_____.

❸ The weather changes from summer

to fall by _____.

❹ Thermometers _____

_____.

What Do You Know?

Talk with a partner.

Draw an object.

Tell about the object.

Solids, Liquids, and Gases

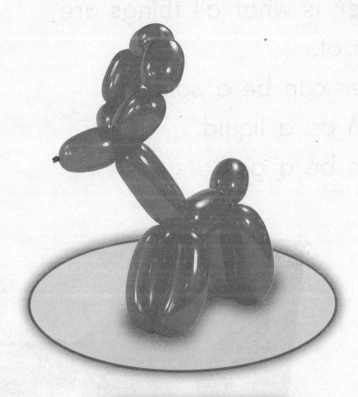

Contents

What Do You Want to Know?

What do you wonder about how objects are different?

_____

_____

_____

_____

_____

_____

117

VOCABULARY

matter What all things are made of. *(noun)*

solid Matter that has its own size and shape. *(noun)*

properties The color, shape, size, and texture of an object. *(noun)*

VOCABULARY ACTIVITY

Find All the Meanings

matter

In "What's the matter?" **matter** means "trouble." **Matter** also means "what all things are made of."

1.a. Students know how solids, liquids, and gases are different.

1 What Are Solids?

Matter is what all things are made of.
Matter can be a solid.
It can be a liquid.
It can be a gas.

What is a solid?
A **solid** has its own size.
It has its own shape.
Rocks are solids.
Bikes are solids.

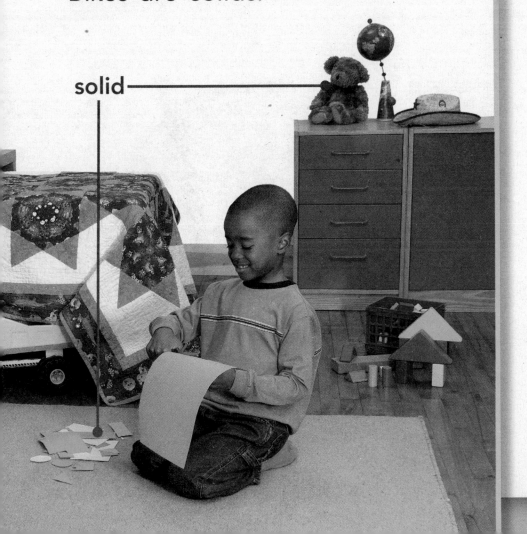

solid ——————

1. Draw an X over all the solid objects in the picture.

2. Write 3 solids from the picture.

    a. _____

    b. _____

    c. _____

3. How can you change the shape of paper?

_____

_____

_____

A solid keeps its shape until you change it.
You can cut paper.
You can break a pencil.
You can bend clay.
These are solids.

pencil

Properties of Solids

Solids have properties.
Properties tell how something looks or feels.
Color and shape are properties.
Size is a property, too.

soft and fuzzy

4. List properties of the pencil.

_____

_____

5. List properties of the slippers.

_____

_____

Summary

A solid keeps its shape until you do something to change it.

Different solids have different properties.

List properties of this rock.

Classify

What are properties you can see?

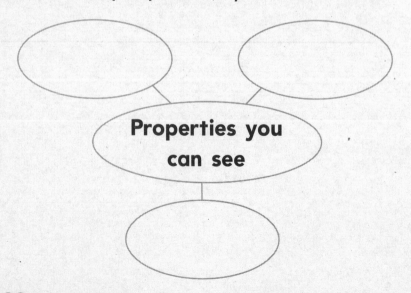

Properties tell what solids do.

Crayons can break.

Rocks sink in water.

These are properties.

rock

Classify

What are properties you can see?

What Are Liquids?

2

Matter can be a liquid.

A **liquid** flows.

You can pour water.

You can pour milk.

These are liquids.

liquid

VOCABULARY

liquid Matter that flows and takes the shape of its container. *(noun)*

VOCABULARY ACTIVITY

Use Words

liquid

You can pour **liquid**.

Use clues from the sentence above to help you understand what **liquid** means.

_____

1.a. Students know how solids, liquids, and gases are different.

123

1. Draw a container. Draw liquid inside the container. Tell about the shape of the liquid.

A liquid takes the shape of its container.
You can change the shape of a liquid.

A solid has its own shape.
A liquid does not.
A liquid changes shape.
It does not always fill its container.

solid

liquid

I **Wonder** . . . I have something in a cup. The cup falls over. What was inside spills out. How can I tell if a solid or liquid was in the cup?

_____

_____

_____

_____

2. Pick two different liquids. Tell about the properties of each liquid.

a. _____

_____

b. _____

_____

Comparing Liquids

Different liquids have different properties. They may be different colors.

Milk is white.

Grape juice is purple.

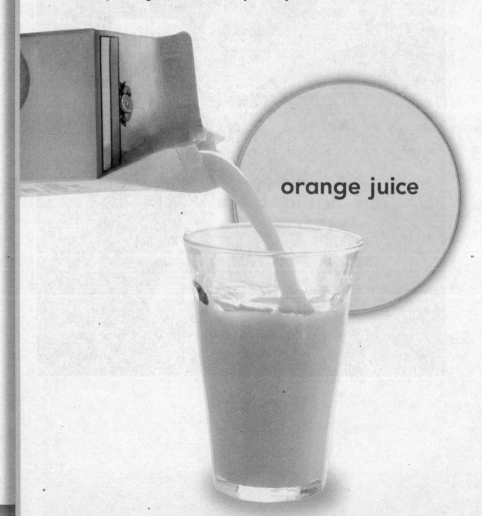

orange juice

Liquids may taste different.
Lemon juice tastes sour.
Apple juice tastes sweet.

sweet honey

Compare

How are solids and liquids different?

Summary

Liquids take the shape of the container they are in.
List different liquids.

Compare How are solids and liquids different?

Solids	Liquids

127

VOCABULARY

gas Matter that spreads out to fill all the space it is in. *(noun)*

VOCABULARY ACTIVITY

Use Words

gas

Gas fills up the balloon.
You fill up the car with **gas**.
Sometimes words have more than one meaning.
See how a word is used in a sentence to tell which meaning to use.

1.a. Students know how solids, liquids, and gases are different.

3 What Are Gases?

Matter can be a gas.
A **gas** fills all the space it is in.
Air is a gas.
It spreads out to fill a hot air balloon.

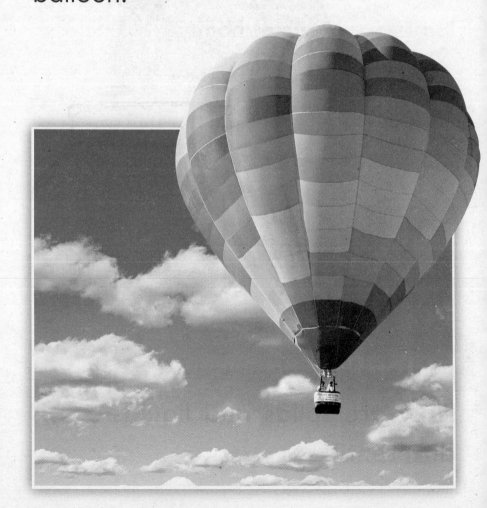

A gas fills a closed container.
It can come out when the
container is opened.
You can feel the gas when you
let it out.
Balloons are filled with gas.

1. Tell how gases and liquids are alike.

_____

_____

_____

2. Tell how gases and liquids are different.

_____

_____

_____

3. Draw a balloon that is filled with air.

4. Show what happens when there is a hole in the balloon.

You cannot see gases.
Gases are all around you.
We breathe the gas called air.
Air fills bubbles, too.

Comparing Gases

Gases can do different things.
Air helps us stay alive.
One kind of gas can heat
a home.
Some gases are used to
cook food.

Main Idea

What are the properties of
a gas?

Summary

Gases are all around you.
Gases spread out to fill a closed
container.
What gas do you need to live?

Main Idea

What are the properties of a gas?

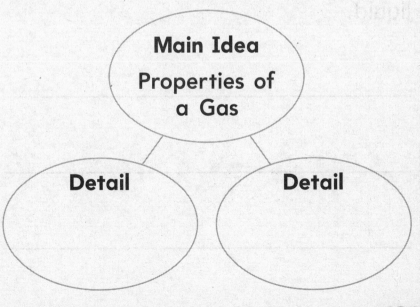

Main Idea
Properties of
a Gas

Detail

Detail

Draw a liquid.

Write a sentence with the word liquid.

_____

_____

_____

gas Matter that spreads out to fill all the space it is in. The balloons are filled with a gas.

gas Materia que se expande hasta rellenar todo el espacio en el que se encuentra. Los globos están lleno de gas.

liquid Matter that flows and takes the shape of its container.

líquido Materia que fluye y toma la forma de su recipiente.

matter What all things are made of.

materia Elementos de los que están hechas todas las cosas.

properties The color, shape, size, and texture of an object. You use your senses to describe an object's properties.

propiedades El color, forma, tamaño y textura de un objeto. Tú utilizas los sentidos para describir las propiedades de un objeto.

solid Matter that has its own size and shape.

sólido Materia que tiene su propia forma y tamaño.

 Visit **www.eduplace.com** to play puzzles and word games.

Find the English words that are like these Spanish words. List the words in the chart.

Spanish Word	English Word
gas	
líquido	
materia	
sólido	

Chapter Review

What Did You Learn?

1 (Circle) the correct answer.

2 Three properties of solids are

_____

_____ .

3 People use gas _____

_____ .

4 Clay is a solid because it _____

_____ .

Responding

Think About What You Have Read

1 All things are made of

_____ .

A) gas

B) matter

C) properties

2 What are three properties of solids?

3 What are some ways people use gas?

4 Is clay a solid? Why?

What Do You Know?

Talk with a partner.

List ways objects change.

_____

_____

_____

_____

Changes in Materials

Contents

What Do You Want to Know?

What do you wonder about how things change?

_____

_____

_____

_____

_____

137

VOCABULARY

energy The power to cause change. *(noun)*

heat A kind of energy that makes things warm. *(noun)*

melt To change from a solid to a liquid. *(verb)*

evaporate To change from a liquid to a gas. *(verb)*

1.b. Students know the properties of matter can change when it is mixed, cooled, or heated.
3.c. Students know the sun warms the land, air, and water.

1 What Does Heating Do?

Energy is the power to change things.
Heat is a kind of energy.
It makes things warm.
Heat from the Sun warms Earth.

Fire gives off heat.

A candle gives off heat.

Rub your hands together.

That makes heat, too.

1. Circle the objects in the pictures that make heat.

2. Circle the words that tell about heat.

3. What makes some solids melt?

_____

I Wonder . . . Heat can change some solids to liquid.
What solids do not melt with heat?

_____

_____

Heat Changes Solids to Liquids

Heat can make matter change.
Heat can make solids melt.
To **melt** is to change from a solid to a liquid.
Heat can melt a juice bar.

Heat Changes Liquids to Gases

Heat can make liquids evaporate. To **evaporate** is to change from a liquid to a gas.

Water evaporates.

Heat made the puddles in the picture evaporate.

Cause and Effect

How can heat change water?

Summary

Energy is the power to cause change.

Heat can make matter change form. What can heat do to ice?

Cause and Effect

How can heat change water?

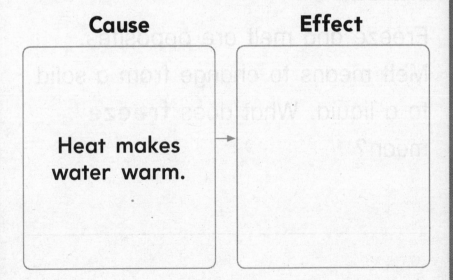

Cause	Effect
Heat makes water warm.	

VOCABULARY

freeze To change from a liquid to a solid. *(verb)*

VOCABULARY ACTIVITY

Use Opposites

freeze

Freeze and melt are opposites. Melt means to change from a solid to a liquid. What does **freeze** mean?

1.b. Students know the properties of matter can change when it is mixed, cooled, or heated.
1.a. Students know how solids, liquids, and gases are different.

2 What Does Cooling Do?

Cooling happens when you take away heat.

Cooling can change matter.

It can make liquids freeze.

To **freeze** is to change from a liquid to a solid.

In winter the air and water are cold.

The water in a pond changes from a liquid to a solid.

liquid solid

Cooling Changes Gases

Cooling can make gases change, too.
Gases change into liquids.
Water as a gas is called water vapor.
There is water vapor in our breath.

water vapor changing to liquid

1. When liquid is cooled, it changes into _____.

2. When gas is cooled, it changes into _____.

Summary

Cooling makes gases change to liquids.

When a liquid cools it changes

into a _____.

⊚ Draw Conclusions

Why does a pond freeze in winter?

Fact
In winter the air temperature is cold.

↓

Fact

↓

Conclusion

144

The air outside a glass is warm. Ice in the glass is cold. Water vapor near the glass cools. It makes drops of water on the glass.

Draw Conclusions

Why does a pond freeze in winter?

What Happens When You Mix Things?

3

A **mixture** is two or more kinds of matter put together.
This snack is a mixture.

mixture

VOCABULARY

mixture Two or more kinds of matter put together. *(noun)*

dissolve To mix completely. *(verb)*

VOCABULARY ACTIVITY

Use Pictures

mixture

Say the word aloud. Use clues from the picture to help you know what **mixture** means.

 1.b. Students know the properties of matter can change when it is mixed, cooled, or heated.
1.a. Students know how solids, liquids, and gases are different.

1. Draw each part of this sandwich.

Mixtures can be taken apart.
A sandwich is a mixture.
It is made of solids.
You can take parts off
your sandwich.

Mixing Solids and Liquids

You can mix a solid and a liquid.
Some solids dissolve in water.
To **dissolve** is to mix completely.
A drink mix dissolves in water.

2. What other solids dissolve
in water?

_____

_____

Summary

A mixture is made of two or more kinds of matter.

You can take apart a mixture.

Name a mixture made of two solids.

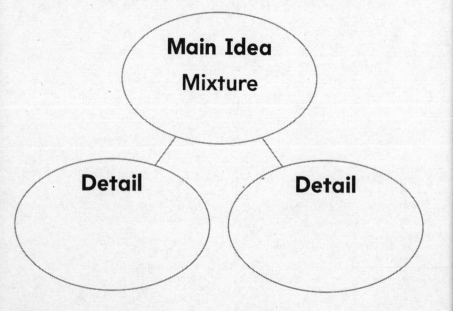 Main Idea

How can you make a mixture?

```
        ┌──────────────┐
        │  Main Idea   │
        │   Mixture    │
        └──────────────┘
         ╱            ╲
   ┌─────────┐    ┌─────────┐
   │ Detail  │    │ Detail  │
   └─────────┘    └─────────┘
```

Mixing Liquids and Gases

You can mix a liquid and a gas.
A fish tank has a mixture of liquid and gas.
The water is a liquid.
The bubbles are air.
Air is a gas.

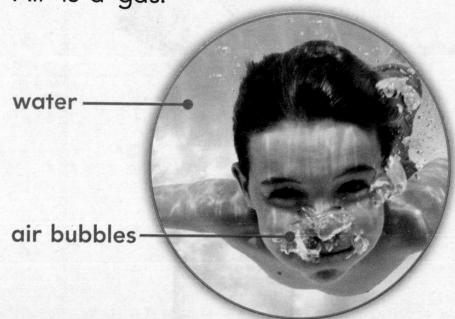

water

air bubbles

Main Idea

How can you make a mixture?

Which Changes Are Not Reversible?

A **reversible change** can be undone.
Some changes are reversible.
Melted ice can be frozen again.
It is reversible.

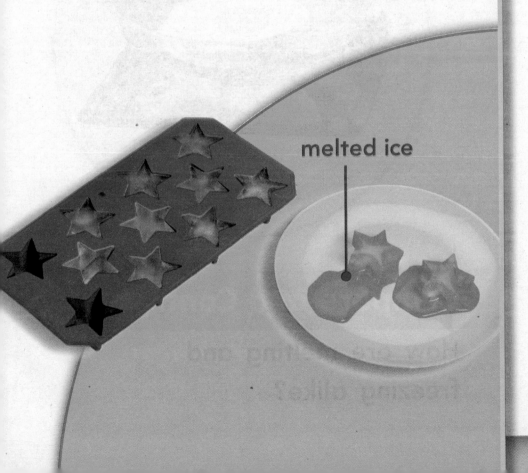

melted ice

VOCABULARY

reversible change A change that can be undone. *(noun)*

VOCABULARY ACTIVITY

Use Words

reversible change

Water can be frozen. Water can melt. Then water can freeze again. This is a **reversible change**. Use clues from the sentences above to help you know what **reversible change** means.

 1.b. Students know the properties of matter can change when it is mixed, cooled, or heated.

149

Summary

A reversible change can be undone.
Some changes are not reversible.
Name a change that cannot be
undone.

_____

_____

◎ Compare and Contrast

How are melting and freezing alike?

Melting	Freezing

Some changes are not reversible.
An egg cannot be uncooked.
It is not reversible.

Compare and Contrast

How are melting and
freezing alike?

dissolve To mix completely.

disolver Mezclar totalmente.

evaporate To change from a liquid to a gas. Heat from the Sun makes puddles evaporate.

evaporar Cambiar de líquido a gas. El calor del Sol hace que los charcos se evaporen.

energy The power to cause change. Energy from the Sun warms land, air, and water.

energía Capacidad de causar cambios. La energía del Sol calienta la tierra, el aire y el agua.

Write the science words that end in silent **e**.

_____

_____

_____

_____

_____

_____

Choose one science word.

Make up a riddle about this word.

Tell the riddle to your partner.

Can he or she guess the word?

freeze To change from a liquid to a solid.

helarse Cambiar de líquido a sólido.

heat A kind of energy that makes things warm. Heat from a stove warms a room.

calor Tipo de energía que caldea las cosas. El calor de una estufa caldea una habitación.

melt To change from a solid to a liquid.

derretirse Cambiar de sólido a líquido.

mixture Two or more kinds of matter put together.

mezcla Dos o más tipos de materia que se juntan.

reversible change A change that can be undone. Melting ice is a reversible change because you can freeze it again.

cambio reversible Un cambio que puede modificarse. Derretir hielo es un cambio reversible, porque puedes producir hielo de nuevo.

 Visit **www.eduplace.com** to play puzzles and word games.

Circle the English words and their meanings for all the science words.

Chapter Review

KWL

What Did You Learn?

1 (Circle) the correct answer.

2 Toys in a box are _____

_____.

3 _____ is a change
that is reversible.

4 Ice cream would _____ if
you left it outside on a sunny day.

Responding

Think About What You Have Read

1 To mix completely is to

_____.

A) dissolve

B) freeze

C) melt

2 Are toys in a toy box a
mixture? Tell why or why not.

3 Name one change that
is reversible.

4 What would happen to ice
cream if you left it outside on
a sunny day?